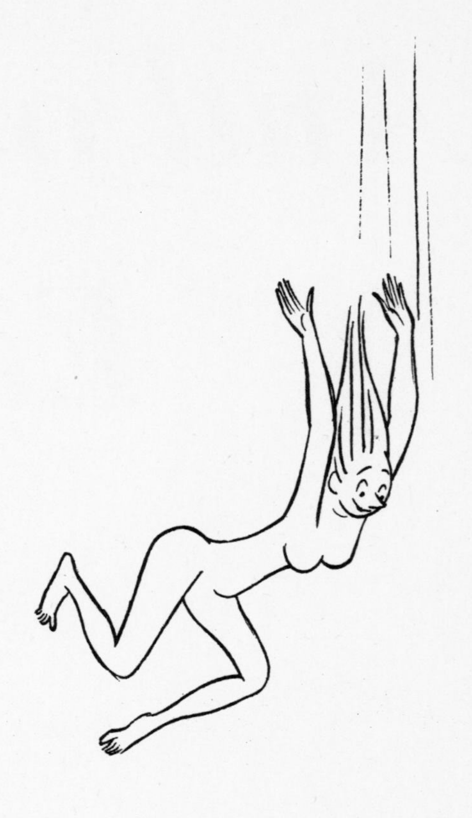

Other books by Abner Dean

IT'S A LONG WAY TO HEAVEN
WHAT AM I DOING HERE?

And on the Eighth Day

by ABNER DEAN

SIMON AND SCHUSTER, NEW YORK

PUBLISHED BY SIMON AND SCHUSTER, INC.
ROCKEFELLER CENTER, 1230 SIXTH AVENUE,
NEW YORK 20, N. Y.

MANUFACTURED IN THE UNITED STATES OF AMERICA
PRINTED BY REEHL LITHO COMPANY
BOUND BY H. WOLFF BOOK MANUFACTURING CO.

TO MY SISTER, ETHEL

TABLE OF CONTENTS

And on the Eighth Day

You make so few demands on yourself

This time it's going to work

The lesson in flying hasn't arrived yet

It's fortunate you don't know how wrong you are

On a clear day the view is awful

Your set of values is different from theirs

This is an age of loose talk

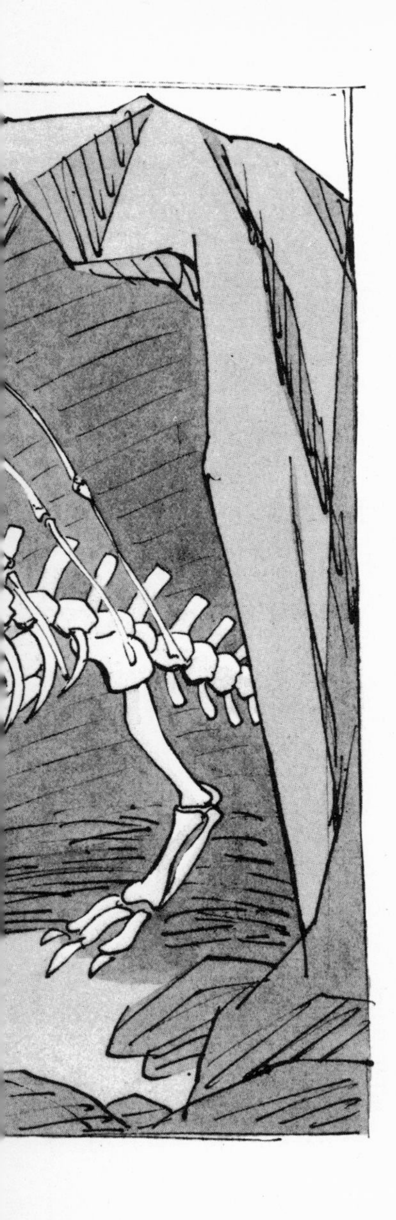

The humorless are the real leaders

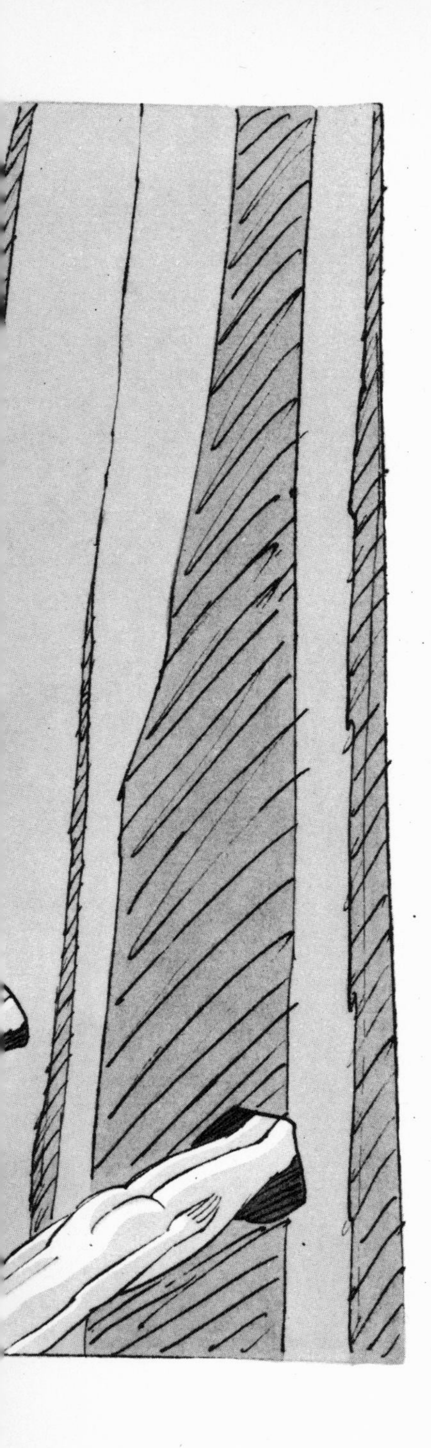

Now you'll have to improvise

They're breeding out the questioners

It's new . . . it's good

The handle came off

She's very sensitive to other people's moods

I wish it were more comfortable

I didn't sell out altogether

Our ancestors had a great sense of humor

You're the opposite sex

A man can be wrong for fifty years . . . or more

The anointed are less complicated

Bad planning did it

It's a limited idea but it will make you a great man

I have entirely different thoughts now

The interpreter makes all the mistakes

You could write a book

Can't they see you're better than they are?

You're a victim of your own environment

No other state of confusion is as interesting as yours

Their arguments are quite forceful

There are no experts yet

You're new, aren't you?

Women are just a symbol

Forward memory

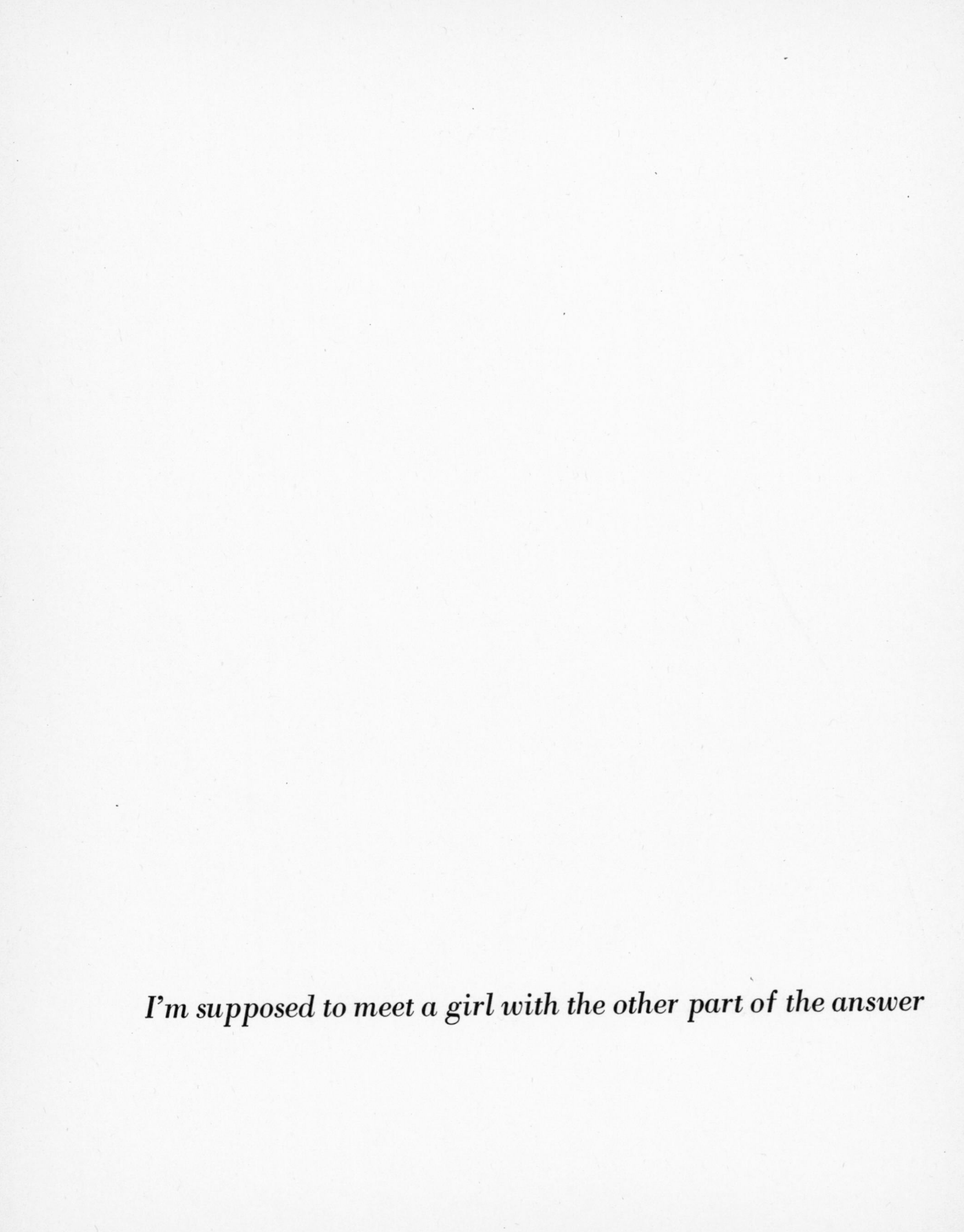

I'm supposed to meet a girl with the other part of the answer

You have ideas of your own

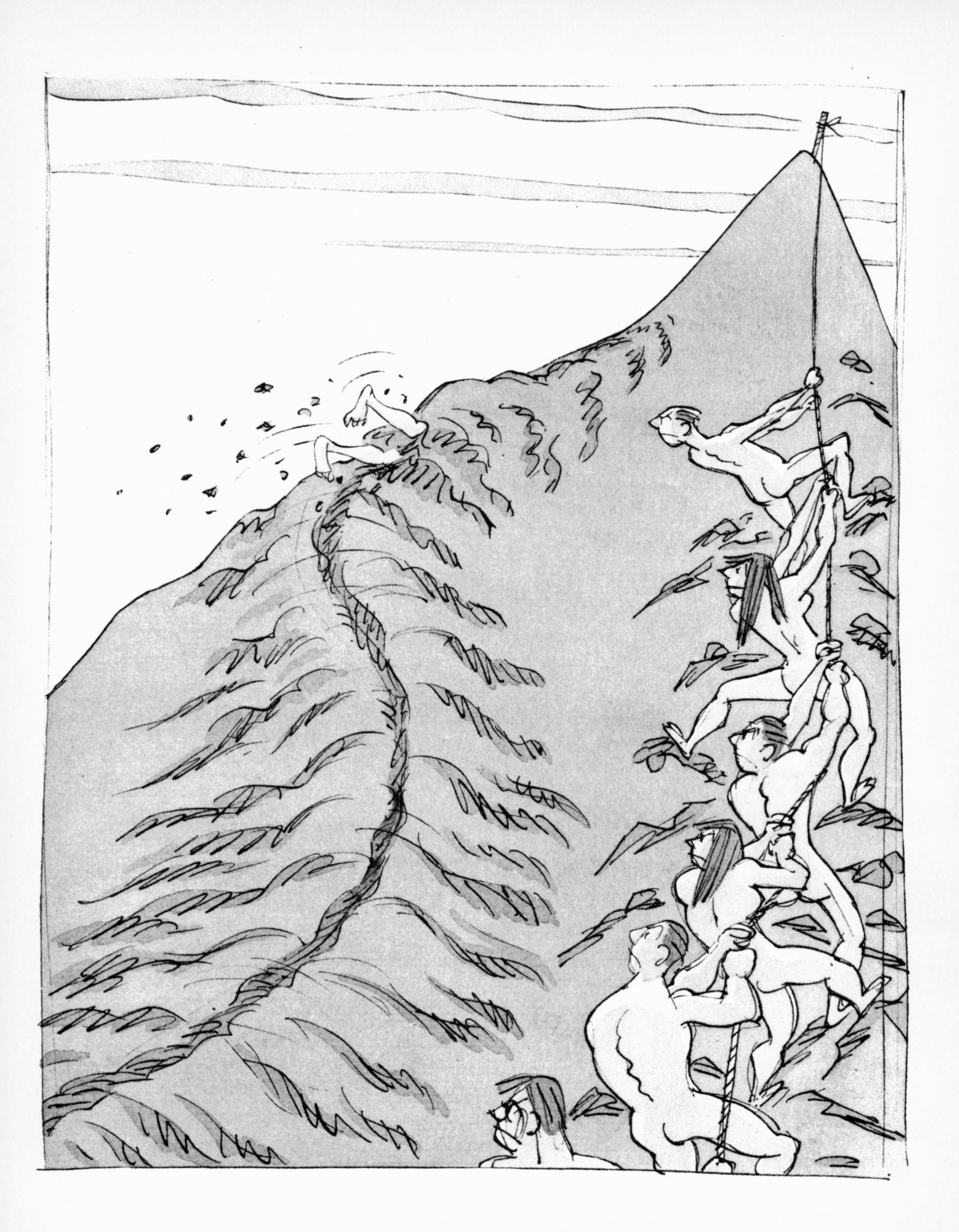

Her eyes have become opaque

Here's the chance you've been waiting for

The guardian of the facts says, "No!"

You're an unsung hero

You have them all fooled

I never knew a woman like you

How do you manage to be right so often?

Come . . . this will be my immortality

Everything was going all right

Be sure you know your way back

Anyone can make a decision

It was easier last time

We need just one more war monument

Things are getting heavier

Does that answer your question?

Don't anyone weep . . . the tragedy is all ours

You're a man of destiny

Repeat after me . . . a million times

What happened in between?

Much too early for value judgments